Book B1

Math Ties

Problem Solving, Logic Teasers, and Math Puzzles

All "Tied" to the Math Curriculum

written by
Terri Husted

illustrated by
Rob Gallerani

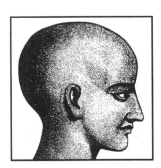

© 1998
CRITICAL THINKING BOOKS & SOFTWARE
www.criticalthinking.com
P.O. Box 448 • Pacific Grove • CA 93950-0448
Phone 800-458-4849 • FAX 831-393-3277
ISBN 0-89455-671-1
Printed in the United States of America

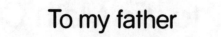

To my father

TABLE OF CONTENTS

(Continued on next page)

Introduction

Math Ties B1 is a classroom-tested approach to help you teach problem solving to *all* your students at middle school level (grades 6–8), regardless of ability. With a track record of 16 successful years, the method provides an organized step-by-step approach to incorporating problem solving on a regular basis in the math classroom, and it includes a collection of problems your students will love to solve.

As a beginning teacher, I realized that learning problem solving is far too complex a process to be developed by giving a short unit or occasional challenge problems. Many students, especially the math anxious or those with previous bad experiences in math, would improve their math skills but make little progress in problem solving. Many had trouble retaining strategies from one year to the next, or even from one lesson to the next. Of the many books available on problem solving, however, none give a methodology for incorporating problem solving as a continuous and integral unit in the math classroom. Also, finding a good collection of problems organized by curriculum themes is nearly impossible without spending an enormous amount of money.

To resolve these issues, I have developed the *Math Ties* problem-solving method. One day a week throughout the entire year is devoted to teaching problem-solving strategies by letting students work on critical-thinking problems in mathematics. I have incorporated the method with classes as large as 36 (for classes larger than 30, it helps to have an assistant). During the rest of the week, I use a variety of methods including lectures and other activities that promote critical thinking, but on problem-solving day, we use *Math Ties* only—and my students love it.

What is problem solving?

To describe this teaching approach, I must first define what problem solving is in mathematics. Problem solving must involve a series of critical-thinking skills. A good problem in mathematics requires some thought process beyond a quick arithmetic solution. It also involves more than just working with word problems, although many word problems are excellent critical-thinking problems. A "problem-solving" problem can be a puzzle, a game, a brainteaser, a logic problem, or any problem that engages the reader in using a strategy. A good problem enhances the concept you have been teaching, promotes discussion, and allows students to enjoy and gain a deeper meaning of mathematics.

The key to teaching critical-thinking skills is that the problem solving must happen as often as possible and must be part of an organized, well-thought-out approach. Learning how to problem solve is a very individual and personal process. Teaching problem solving requires step-by-step modeling, gradual presentation of strategies, many opportunities for students to practice the same strategy with many different types of problems, constant practice in a nonthreatening environment, follow-up time for reflection on each problem, and—that rare occurrence in most math classrooms—time allowed for long-term growth (not all students learn at the same rate). Moreover, problem solving works best when it is taught in the context of the topic being learned and should include, whenever possible, a multicultural component.

The goals of *Math Ties* are for all students to (1) become more proficient in using problem-solving strategies (see pp. xi, xii); (2) attempt all problems without giving up right away; (3) gain confidence in their math ability and become more independent; (4) see connections between problems, between topics, and between disciplines; and (5) see solving problems as a challenge and not as an overwhelming obstacle, whether in math class or in everyday life.

One problem-solving strategy is the use of manipulatives. My room is equipped with blocks, tiles, construction paper, markers, scissors, glue, toothpicks, scrap paper, rulers, compasses, calculators, and large poster paper so that students can diagram the problem, make cutouts, and move "people" about (in bridge problems, etc.). I don't have expensive manipulatives; many of my students like creating their own while solving a problem. I often encourage students to dramatize the problem because acting out a problem is fun and helps students see parts of the problem not previously seen.

Whether you use *Math Ties* once a week or more, what is most important is that you do it consistently throughout the year. This may seem impossible with so much curriculum to cover, but most of the problems you will use are enrichment problems from your curriculum that will enhance and expand what you are already teaching. The *Math Ties* problem-solving day will be the highlight of the week for you and your students. With reinforcement, modeling of strategies, and honest praise, students learn to explore their critical-thinking capabilities as they never have before, and they learn to love mathematics.

At the beginning of the year, I give my students a Math Myths survey (see p. 71) to understand their preconceived notions about math. I constantly remind my students that mathematics does not belong to the well-known scientists or the brightest minds; mathematics belongs to every one of us. Becoming good at problem solving takes time and practice, but it requires more than a good collection of problems. It also takes clear expectations, lots of planning, and a well-structured environment that is warm and caring and where students can be free from fear of failure.

Choosing the problems

I choose my problems according to curriculum themes (see Table of Contents, p. iii, Matrix of Problem-Solving Concepts, p. 72, and Matrix of Problem-Solving Strategies, p. 75). I have numbered the problems in the matrix only to help you determine what concepts and problem-solving strategies are covered by each problem. You can use the problems in any order that best fits your curriculum and the needs of your students. However, during the first week I usually begin with logic problems and classic brainteasers so I can learn more about the students' math abilities, their group work behavior, their level of math anxiety, and their social skills. Kin problems are also great problems to start with because students love them and they clearly demonstrate the importance of making diagrams.

This collection includes the most successful problems I have used in middle school. Variations of these problems can be found in brainteaser books, history of math books, enrichment sections of textbooks, math contests, etc. Many of the problems are contributions made by fellow teachers, students, parents, and even friends and neighbors. Some problems work better with certain levels, and it is important to document those results. Many younger students and students who are not very motivated in math do better if they start with problems that require manipulatives, dramatization, cutting, pasting, and coloring. It is the task of a good math teacher to get all students to engage in mathematical discussions and to encourage students to use mathematical vocabulary whenever possible. Some students, at first, are not comfortable with problems that require sophisticated explanations and open discussion among peers. Be patient. Most students need to gain some confidence before engaging in any activity that requires risk-taking. Some of the best thinking strategies I have seen have come from those labeled "lower-level" students. It is very important to validate each student's response and effort.

How to get started

Set up your classroom in groups of 2 to 4 students (3–4 is best). Any student who wants to work alone should be gently encouraged to work in a group. Groups larger than 4 are often too large. I let students choose their own group, but I do make changes as needed.

Math Ties includes enough material for at least two problems per session for a 36-week school year. You should augment this number to four or five problems per session by collecting additional problems throughout the year. Select the problems you will use for a one-period class, and cut them separately in strips, allowing one problem per student.

The beginning of class is a good time to discuss a problem-solving strategy. I have included a problem-solving concept map that you can use with your students to model how to solve a problem. Make copies of the problem-solving strategies and the concept map, and have students refer to them during each session. I have a large section of my wall devoted to problem solving where I can post the strategies, the group rules, and many samples of the students' work.

The class comes in on problem-solving day and waits to hear me read the first (or my favorite) problem aloud. During this quiet time, I review group rules and alert them to try certain strategies that may be most useful for that day's session. Each group is then asked to choose a team leader. Reading the first problem aloud promotes interest and gets the students excited about starting. I hand out a copy of the first problem to each person in the room. The rest of the problems are spread out on a table (one copy of each problem for every student). This consistent method of starting helps maintain a structured environment.

The job of the team leader is to keep the group on task and to go to the table to get a copy of the next problem for each person in the group. Allow the team leader to get only one problem at a time; otherwise, the members of the group are likely to work on several different problems at the same time, and that's the end of cooperation and good discussion among team members. Stress that it is not necessary to do *all* the problems—it is more important to work carefully on each one. Once they have experienced problems with more than one answer (see A Wolf, A Goat, and A Cabbage, p. 2) and found that the first answer is not usually the correct one, they will become more cautious. Soon they will start reading each problem more carefully, which is one of the goals of problem solving.

To grade or not to grade

Becoming good at problem solving takes time, but it is a skill that all students can develop with practice. Some students have a negative attitude towards math problems, and many (including adults) strongly dislike word problems. Many students have had bad experiences with word problems because of poor reading skills, poor math skills, attitudes shared by peers (or even parents), lack of practice, and previous failures. Many students fear getting stuck and appearing "stupid" in front of their peers. Some avoid even starting a problem because they are convinced that others are always better than they are at solving problems. They fear the time pressure and a low or failing grade. Nevertheless, many teachers are reluctant to try anything without attaching a grade to the activity; they fear that students won't work unless they "have to." I strongly recommend that problem solving *not* be graded. Students will take risks, enjoy the activities, and seek you out for more problems if the fear of a grade is lifted. As long as the problem-solving experience is free from the pressures of a grade, students will develop many or all of the problem-solving strategies in my list, given time and experience. I am convinced that a nonthreatening environment in the classroom is crucial to the success of developing good critical-thinking skills in mathematics.

You can evaluate each student's progress by keeping an index card on each student, recording notes on progress, or giving extra credit for problems done individually at home. You can give extra credit to those students who expand, rewrite, or diagram the problem on a poster, etc. It may be difficult to walk around taking notes on students' responses and progress. Therefore, you may occasionally want to use the Problem-Solving Interpretation (p. xiii) and Analysis of Solutions (p. xiv) forms with a problem of your choice or one chosen by the student, in order to analyze how students attack problems. You can hand out these sheets the last fifteen minutes of class and ask students to pick one problem to analyze. You will learn an enormous amount about mathematics acquisition and critical thinking by listening to students' comments and explanations.

Portfolios offer another evaluation method. Have students create a portfolio of problems they choose according to several categories (see Appendix A for the student forms). The worksheets are designed to encourage students to reflect on their growth. Keep their problems in a folder so they can take them home, and let them choose the problems for their final portfolio to turn in to you at a later time. Be careful not to let the portfolio work or any critical-thinking evaluation sheets become the goal of the problem-solving unit. The goal is for your students to experience many types of problems, enjoy problem solving, and become stronger at it.

The teacher's role during problem solving

The role of the teacher in a problem-solving session is that of facilitator, role model, and guide. You must make sure that the problem-solving rules are being followed. The level of noise in the classroom is bound to be higher, but students will work and follow the rules if you set clear expectations and review the rules periodically. One way to avoid students' calling out is to use the "red and green" cups. Tape together the bottoms of two cups, one green and one red, so that students can put the red side up when they need help and keep the green side up when they do not need help. One "red and green" cup is used per group. You can experiment creating some other device that students can use to let you know they need help without having to call you or raise their hands. Try not to answer any questions for the first ten minutes of class; your silence encourages the group to check with each other. Also, if you are unable to come over right away, students will keep on working and often end up not needing help. Try not to answer questions unless everyone in the group has been consulted and the entire group needs a hint in order to continue working.

When the group comes up with an answer, expect an explanation. You need not always tell them if they are correct. Eventually, they won't check for approval once they are satisfied that their answer is correct. Some problems have more than one answer, so encourage your students to find other solutions. For some problems, the group's final answer may not be the most efficient. Always accept and praise original solutions, but ask students to stick to the restrictions given by the problem.

Classroom discipline

There are several ways to maintain good classroom discipline when doing a problem-solving session. The classroom will not be quiet, but it should not be so noisy that students have problems communicating within their own group. Students must learn to stay in their group and not visit other groups. Here are some ways to avoid discipline problems:

1. Frequently review rules and expectations at the beginning of the session.

2. Allow only the team leader to get up. Don't allow visiting between groups.

3. Stop all students a few minutes before class is over so they can clean up, put problems in a folder (or you may collect them from each group yourself), and straighten up the room.

4. Allow students to work with some of their friends. Students forced to sit with someone they strongly dislike can end up hating group work. Social conflicts are more frequent in middle school, so use your best judgment and, above all, be fair and consistent. Some students need to work together with the same set of students for a few sessions to feel more comfortable. Change groups only when there is good reason to. Teachers may disagree on how to set up groups, so try several approaches and choose what works best for you.

Don't expect perfection the first few times you try this approach; it will take time. If you are enthusiastic about problem-solving day with *Math Ties*, your students will be as well.

What to do with the problems that are solved

Students can keep all their solved problems in a neat pile on their group table with their names on them and turn the problems in at the end of the period. Hang as many problems as possible on the wall. Encourage students to extend the problem, diagram results, or create a poster of the problem for extra credit. If a group has finished all the problems, they can start on their homework or you may give them an extra problem to solve. Many students enjoy taking problems home for their parents to solve. Don't forget to give feedback to the parents and also hang the results in your classroom. Follow-up discussions are very important; a good time for the discussion is the next day at the beginning of class.

Above all, praise and praise

With continuous reinforcement throughout the year, a warm and caring environment, freedom from fear of failure, great problems to solve, and constant honest praise, students will grow at problem solving and learn to love mathematics.

GROUP RULES FOR PROBLEM SOLVING

1. Stay in groups of 2, 3, or 4.

2. Everyone must participate.

3. Work together as a group. Do not let anyone in your group get behind or ahead.

4. Use the problem-solving strategies posted.

5. Help those in your group who do not understand, but do not do the work for them.

6. Be a good listener. Do not make fun of anyone's ideas.

7. Do not ask for help until everyone in your group has been consulted and has no idea how to proceed. Keep working until the teacher gets to you.

8. Remember, there is often more than one way to solve a problem.

9. Team leaders: Keep your group on task and come get the next problem when everyone is ready.

10. It's OK not to do all the problems. Relax and enjoy math!

PROBLEM-SOLVING STRATEGIES

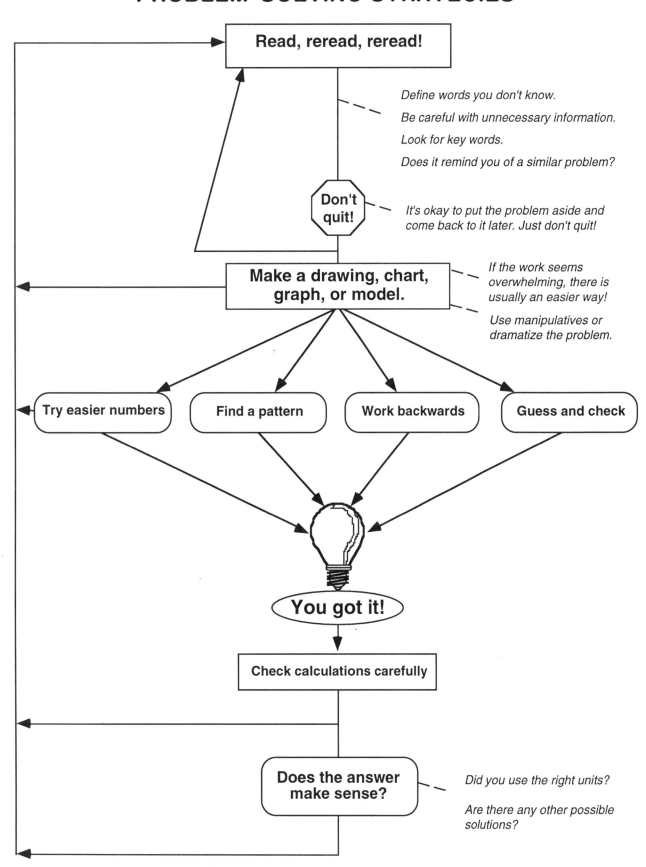

Read, reread, reread!

Define words you don't know.

Be careful with unnecessary information.

Look for key words.

Does it remind you of a similar problem?

Don't quit!

It's okay to put the problem aside and come back to it later. Just don't quit!

Make a drawing, chart, graph, or model.

If the work seems overwhelming, there is usually an easier way!

Use manipulatives or dramatize the problem.

Try easier numbers   **Find a pattern**   **Work backwards**   **Guess and check**

You got it!

Check calculations carefully

Does the answer make sense?

Did you use the right units?

Are there any other possible solutions?

PROBLEM-SOLVING STRATEGIES

Read, reread, and reread

1. Say the problem aloud. Explain it in your own words to someone else.

2. Before you start, be sure you understand what is being asked.

3. Define any words you don't know.

4. Look for key words, but be sure to read in context.

5. Be careful with unnecessary information.

6. Think of a similar problem you've solved before.

7. Don't quit! It's okay to put the problem aside and come back to it later.

Attack the problem

8. Use manipulatives or dramatize the problem.

9. Make a drawing, chart, graph, or model.

10. Take a guess and check your answer.

11. Find a pattern or formula.

12. Try easier numbers. Sometimes this helps you find a pattern.

13. Work backwards.

14. If the work seems overwhelming, there is usually a much easier way to solve it.

Check your answer

15. Check your calculations carefully. Did you use the correct unit?

16. Did you answer the question being asked?

17. Read the problem again; does the answer make sense?

18. Are there any other possible answers you did not consider?

PROBLEM-SOLVING INTERPRETATION

Problem Title _____

State the problem in your own words:

Diagram the problem:

ANALYSIS OF SOLUTIONS

Problem Title _____

I tried these solutions, and they didn't work: Why not:

THIS SOLUTION WORKED!

CROSSING THE RIVER

To the teacher

Your students will love dramatizing these problems; they are great for teaching the importance of making diagrams and charts. Note that, for problems 2 and 3, students should count each way across the river as "one trip."

To learn more about the origin of the problems like the ones in this section, read *Ethnomathematics* (pp. 109–116) by Marcia Ascher. Tell your students that there are many versions of The Wolf, the Goat, and the Cabbage problem in different cultures and that many appear in African story puzzles. Many cultures enjoy doing logic problems and use mathematics for their everyday needs as well as for enjoyment!

Problem 4, The Four Middle School Students, was contributed by Fred Paul, retired Director of Mathematics, NYS Department of Education, Albany.

1   A WOLF, A GOAT, AND A CABBAGE

A wolf, a goat, and a cabbage must be moved across a river in a boat holding only one besides the ferryman. How must he carry them across so that the goat shall not eat the cabbage, nor the wolf the goat? (The wolf does not eat cabbage.)

2   THE THREE JEALOUS HUSBANDS

Three men who are traveling with their wives come to a river they must cross. On the shore, they find a boat that can carry only two people at a time. Since all the husbands are very jealous, no woman can be left with a man unless her husband is present. How many trips does it take to cross the river? Count each way as one trip. The boat must be brought back each time.

3 THE THREE CATS AND THE THREE MICE

Three cats and three mice leave town and travel together. They come to a river they must cross. The only boat they find can carry only two at a time. The mice will get eaten if there are more cats than mice on either shore. What is the minimum number of trips it will take for all of them to cross safely? (Remember, the boat must be brought back and you need to worry only about the number of cats and mice *on the shore*). Count each way as one trip.

4 THE FOUR MIDDLE SCHOOL STUDENTS

A group of 4 DeWitt Middle School students wish to cross a bridge without siderails in the middle of a jungle very late at night. They have one lantern to share. No one may take a step without holding the lantern (it's a dark night with no moon). No more than two people may be on the bridge at one time, not even for a moment. What is the shortest time it would take for all of them to get across? Use the following information to solve the problem:

The first student can cross the bridge alone in 5 minutes. (She's a track star.)

The second can cross the bridge alone in 10 minutes.

The third can cross the bridge alone in 20 minutes.

The fourth can cross the bridge alone in 25 minutes. (He has a broken foot.)

When two students walk together, they must move at the rate of the slower person!

KIN PROBLEMS

To the teacher

"Relations" is an important concept, as the relationship of one quantity to another forms the basis for much of mathematics. These problems on family relationships will make students read and reread. Good knowledge of verbs and adjectives and the use of apostrophes may be the key to understanding expressions such as "this man's father is my father's son." Be sure you ask students to demonstrate their answers, and encourage them to make diagrams. Note that some problems may have more than one right answer. (I was convinced I had the correct answer to "Bermuda" until one of my students showed me a different solution!)

Issues of family structure may come up during this problem-solving session, so you need to be sensitive to children who have no siblings or have only one parent. They need to be reassured that they can use their own family structure as an example, too.

Before handing out the problems, tell your students that family relationship puzzles are very popular in many cultures. For more on kin problems, read Marcia Ascher's book *Ethnomathematics*, Chapter 3.

You may find these problems so intriguing that you'll wish to share some (i.e., From Bermuda…) with your English colleagues.

5 FROM BERMUDA

A man is looking at a picture of a person on the wall. He says: " Brothers and sisters I have none, but this man's father is my father's son." Who is the man looking at? (Draw a picture to help you.)

6 FROM PUERTO RICO

Who is the sister of my aunt, who is not my aunt but is the daughter of my grandparents? (Draw a picture.)

FROM WALES

My mother has only one sibling. What relation to us is a brother-in-law to the only brother of our mother? (Draw a picture.)

 # FROM THE UNITED STATES

How close a relative is the sister-in-law of your father's only (unmarried) brother? (Draw a picture.)

9 FROM BRAZIL

Two mothers and two daughters sleep in the same room. There are only three beds and each one sleeps on one of them. How can this be? (Draw a picture.) (Ascher, p. 69)

10 FROM IRELAND

One day three brothers were going past a graveyard. One of them said: "I shall go in so that I may pray for the soul of my brother's son." The second man said the same thing. The third brother said: "I shall not go in, my brother's son is not there." Who is buried in the graveyard? (Draw a picture.) (Ascher. p. 69)

LOGIC PROBLEMS

To the teacher

These problems are classic logic problems, variations of which have been around for many centuries. The fact that they are still popular shows how much fun they are to solve! I use these problems at the beginning of the year because they help students get to know each other; they also encourage students to read and reread.

To help students get started on "Who's Telling the Truth?" ask them to consider all the possibilities (what if the guide is a truth-teller and the native is a truth-teller; what if the guide is a truth-teller but the native is a liar; etc.) and write them down.

Students love to act out both the "Three Intelligent Women" problem and the "Apples and Oranges" problem. For the former, use small stickers they can put on their foreheads (no pen marks!). For the latter, you might want to have some boxes with apples and oranges for a great snack.

11   THE THREE INTELLIGENT WOMEN

Three intelligent women were applying for a computer job for which they were equally qualified. The interviewer, who was also pretty smart, decided that the job would go to the applicant who first solved a logic problem, as described below. The three applicants were

blindfolded while a mark was placed on their foreheads. They were then told that each of them had either a black or white mark on her forehead. Each was told to raise her hand, when the blindfolds were taken off, if she saw a black mark on the forehead of either of the other two. The first one to tell the color of the mark on her own forehead (and how she arrived at the answer) would get the job. The blindfolds were taken off...and all three women raised their hands at the same time! One of them came up with the color of her own mark. What color is her mark, and how did she figure it out?

12   WHO'S TELLING THE TRUTH?

Two tribes live on an island. Those who live on the western side always tell the truth, and those who live on the eastern side always lie. A scientist who visits the island hires a native in the center of the island as a guide to help her get around, but she wants to keep him only if he is a truth-teller. She thinks of a plan and says to the guide, "Please, go ask that other native over there which side he lives on." When the guide returns he tells the scientist, "He says he lives on the western side." Was the guide a truth-teller or a liar? How can you tell?

13   APPLES AND ORANGES

Three boxes are labeled "Apples," "Oranges," and "Apples & Oranges." Someone has played a joke by mixing up the labels, and now each label is incorrect. You may put your hand into only one box and pull out only one fruit—hey, no peeking or feeling what is inside! Which box would you pick from if you could pick only one fruit?

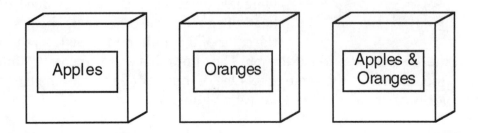

14   THE FAMOUS CARD PROBLEM

Four pieces of cardboard have either **blue** or **yellow** on one side, and each one has either a circle or a triangle on the other side. Here's what they look like on a table:

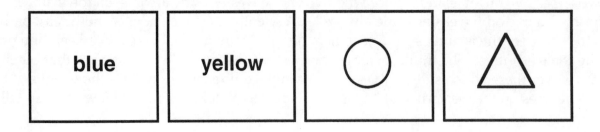

Which cards (minimum number) must you pick up and turn over in order to have sufficient information to answer this question: Does every blue card have a triangle on its other side?

15 THE SIX GLASSES

Six glasses, three filled with water and three empty, are shown below. If you can touch only one glass, how can you arrange them so that the filled and the empty glasses alternate (full, empty, full, empty, full, empty)? No magic tricks!

EXPONENTS AND FRACTIONS

To the teacher

The problems in this section will enrich your lessons on exponents and fraction concepts. Encourage students to make diagrams and find patterns and, for the work on exponents, use their calculators. The fraction work is simple, and students should be able to do it without a calculator.

To demonstrate the Bookworm problem, you might want to have some books handy, or use manipulatives.

16 ST. IVES

As I was going to St. Ives, I met a man with seven wives (they were all going to St. Ives, too). Every wife had seven sacks. Every sack had seven cats. Every cat had seven kittens. How many wives, sacks, cats, and kittens were going to St. Ives?

17 TERRI'S GRANDFATHER

Terri asked her grandfather: "How old are you now, Grandpa?" He said, "I've lived a quarter of my life as a boy, a sixth of my life as a young man, half of my life as a middle-aged man; all those years I spent in my native country. Now, you must add the past six years I've spent as a new immigrant." How old is Terri's grandfather?

18   YOUR ANCESTORS

If you could ask your relatives from the past ten generations to come to dinner at your house (and they could come!), how many would you expect to entertain? (Invite only your parents, grandparents, etc., no uncles, cousins, or other relatives.)

Can you find a formula that will give the grand total in one step?

19   A PLUMBING PROBLEM

The diagram below shows part of a plumbing unit that provides water to your school. Two-thirds of the water entering through Pipe 1 goes through Pipe 2; the rest goes through Pipe 3. One-quarter of the water in Pipe 2 goes through Pipe 4. What fraction of the water entering through Pipe 1 actually exits through Pipe 4?

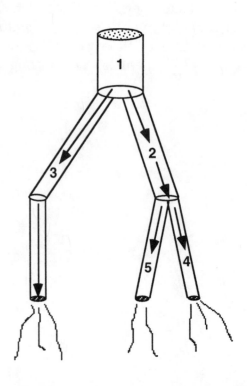

20   BOOKWORM

The first three volumes of a set of math problem-solving books are standing upright and in order on a bookshelf. Each book has one-eighth-inch covers and one inch of pages. A bookworm starts at the first page of Volume I and eats its way to the last page of Volume II. How far does the bookworm travel?

PRE-ALGEBRA/ALGEBRA

To the teacher

These problems can be solved not only by students who know equations and are learning systems of equations, they also offer students without knowledge of equations a chance to explore algebra concepts. The more they think about the concepts, the more comfortable students will be once they start algebra. "Another Day, Another Dollar" is an excellent problem to dramatize. Students may feel confused after reading it, but once they act it out they will see that there was no extra dollar that mysteriously "disappeared."

21 CENTI, THE CENTIPEDE

Centi, the centipede, was down a well 10 feet deep. Starting November 29, Centi climbed 2 feet and dropped 1 foot daily. On which day did Centi's head reach ground level?

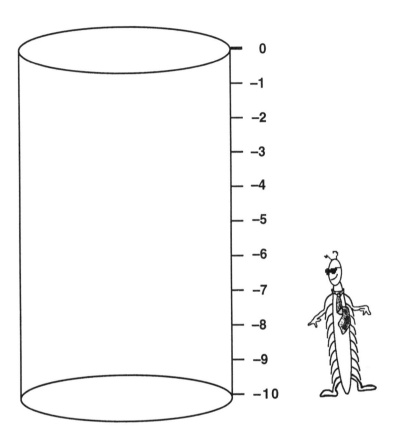

22 THE BABY WHALE

A baby whale weighs 100 pounds plus half its weight. How much does it weigh?

23 VISITING GRANDMA

Elise and her brother were visiting their grandmother in Florida. Gaby is twice as old as his sister Elise, and their grandmother is three times as old as Gaby. If the ages of all three total 90 years, can you determine their ages? (Using the symbol below to represent Elise's age, show the symbols that represent the other two ages.)

Elise

24 UNUSUAL PET SHOP

In a small town, there is a pet shop that has only birds and dogs. If there are 30 pets and they have a total of 86 legs, how many of these pets are birds? (Assume that all dogs have four legs.)

25   A FARMER'S PROBLEM

A farmer in New York picks apples on three successive days. Each day she picks two times as many apples as on the previous day. Over the three-day period, she picks 700 apples. How many does she pick on the second day?

26   JACK AND JILL'S BOOK PROBLEM

Jack and Jill together have 29 paperback books. If Jack lost three of his books and Jill doubled her supply, the two of them together would have 40 books. How many does each have now? (Make a chart to help you).

27 ANOTHER DAY, ANOTHER DOLLAR

Three business women need to rent a car for one day. The cost is $30 so they each pay $10. As they approach their rental car, the owner at the counter says, "Wait, there's been a change. It's your lucky day. The fee is only $25. Here's $5 back." Since the women are in a hurry and do not want to split the $5, they give the owner a $2 tip and they keep $3. So, each woman paid $10 – $1 (money they each got back) = $9, times 3 is $27. If you add the $2 tip, you get only $29! Where is the extra dollar? Explain.

GEOMETRY

To the teacher

Students who are visual learners will enjoy working with these problems. Encourage your students to take time to think these problems through instead of just guessing. Some of the problems (such as "What Angle Is It?") seem very simple but are not. Have ready blocks to use for manipulatives, a Styrofoam™ block to demonstrate the "Carpenter's problem," and a box with some string to simulate the path of the fly for the "Geometry Fly" problem. Some students may want to create the demonstration models themselves; you could then use the preformed models with other classes.

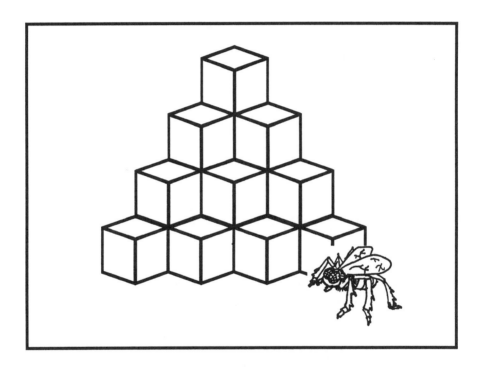

28 THINKING IN QUARTERS

How many quarter-inch squares does it take to make an inch square? (Draw it with a ruler.)

How many quarter-inch cubes does it take to make an inch cube? (Build it!)

29 A CARPENTER'S PROBLEM

A carpenter wants to cut this wooden cube into 27 equal cubes. What is the minimum number of cuts she needs to make?

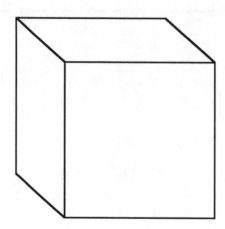

30   CUBES IN THE CORNER

At a store display, identical cubes are stacked in the corner as shown. How many of the cubes are *not* visible?

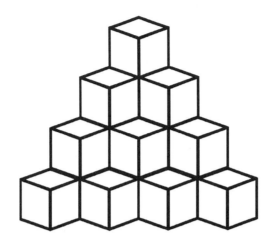

Suppose there were an additional layer with 5 blocks visible on the bottom. Then how many of the cubes would not be visible?

31   WHAT ANGLE IS IT?

What angle do the hands of a clock really make at 3:30?

32 REGIONS IN A CIRCLE

What is the maximum number of regions into which a circle may be divided by three straight lines? By four straight lines? By five straight lines? Can you describe a pattern?

33 THE MISSING DIAMETER

Can you find the diameter of the circle below? Rectangle ABCD is shown below. C is the center of the circle. BD = 8.5″ and DE = 3″. Explain your answer.

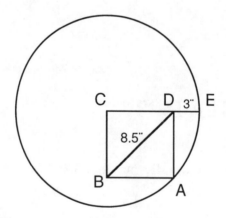

34   A DIFFERENT VIEW

What is the circumference of the semicircle inscribed in the rectangle shown below? Explain how you arrived at your answer.

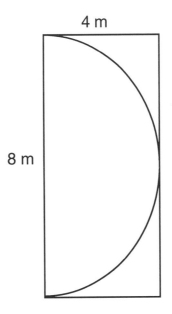

35   THE MISSING PERIMETER

Find the perimeter of the figure below if the angles shown are 90 degrees.

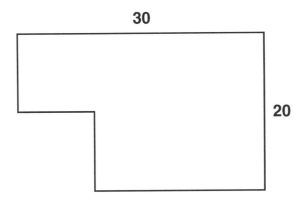

36 THE GEOMETRY FLY

A fly that has lived in your math class for several years flies only in straight lines! If your classroom is shown below and it has the dimensions shown, what distance does the fly travel if it flies from point E to point C?

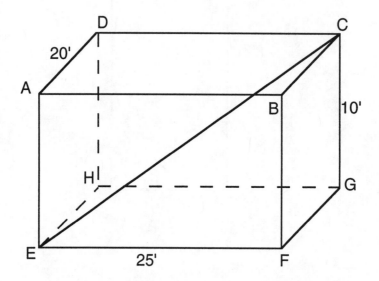

NUMBER THEORY

To the teacher

These are great problems for experimenting with patterns and enjoying work with numbers. Make sure to review the definitions of "sum," "difference," "product," "quotient," and "remainder," as well as the differences between "factors" and "multiples."

On the shortcut problems, ask students to find a method for determining the answer without using a calculator. The Census Taker problem will seem impossible to solve at first. Encourage students to start writing combinations of numbers that are factors of 36. Remember, many students are not used to working at problems they cannot figure out right away. You may want to use Problem 40 when teaching perfect squares and square roots—it offers a beautiful pattern for students to discover! Students may at first feel overwhelmed with Problem 42. Review the problem-solving strategies, and tell them that if a problem seems overwhelming or time-consuming, they should look for a shortcut or pattern.

37 THE SUM FROM 1 TO 20

Find a shortcut for adding all the numbers from 1 to 20.

38 THE SUM FROM 1 TO 99

Can you find a shortcut for finding the sum of all numbers from 1 to 99?

$$1 + 2 + 3 + 4 + ... + 96 + 97 + 98 + 99$$

39　THE SUM FROM 4 TO 180

Find a shortcut to get the sum of all numbers from 4 to 180 inclusive (including 4 and 180).

40　THE FIRST 50 ODD NUMBERS

Find a shortcut for finding the sum of the first 50 odd numbers.

41   **THE 450th ODD NUMBER?**

Find a shortcut for determining the 450th odd number.

42   **2^{50} (TWO TO THE 50th POWER)**

Find a shortcut for determining the remainder when 2^{50} is divided by 3.

43 THE CENSUS TAKER

A census taker stopped at a lady's house and wanted to find out how many children she had. The lady, a math teacher, wanted to see if the census taker still knew his math.

Census taker to lady: How many children do you have?

Lady: Three

Census taker: How old are they?

Lady: The product of their ages is 36.

Census taker: That's not enough information.

Lady: The sum of their ages is our house number.

Census taker (looking at the house number): Still not enough information.

Lady: My oldest child plays the piano.

Census taker: Aha! I know now. Thank you!

How did the census taker figure out their ages? Can *you*? Don't quit! Start by trying some numbers.

The three ages: _____ _____ _____

SET THEORY

To the teacher

Students need to become familiar with union and intersection of sets before doing these problems. Model a few simpler examples. Using Venn diagrams is an organized way of solving many problems in mathematics and gives students another strategy they can choose. You can also use Venn diagrams when you do your lesson on the number system (categorizing rationals, irrationals, integers, whole numbers, counting or natural numbers, even integers and odd integers).

I've included a simple diagram for students to use in creating their own problems.

44 ### THE SIXTH GRADE MUSICAL

Many middle school students are known for their musical talent. In the 6th grade class, 62 students take band, 71 take choir, and 46 take orchestra. Of those who take band, 20 take choir but not orchestra. Seven students take band and orchestra but not choir. Six students take choir and orchestra but not band, and five students take all three. Twenty students do not take band, orchestra, or choir because they couldn't fit it into their schedules. How many students are in the 6th grade class?

45 ### THE ANTIQUE BUTTON COLLECTION

Mike's mother has an antique button collection. She has seven triangular buttons. She has six solid yellow buttons and three solid blue buttons. She also has six buttons that are square. Her most expensive button is blue/yellow, and it is not triangular or square. Of the triangular buttons, two are solid yellow and one is solid blue. Of the square buttons, two are solid blue and three are solid yellow. One solid yellow button is not triangular or square. Can you determine how many buttons are in her collection?

46 THE MOTOR CLUB

If you know the following about the members, how many women belong to the motor club?

      1) Twelve drive a car and/or a motorcycle.

      2) Eighteen do not drive a car and/or do not drive a motorcycle.

      3) Eight drive a car.

      4) Two drive a car and a motorcycle.

47 CREATE YOUR OWN SETS PROBLEM

Create your own sets problem using this diagram.

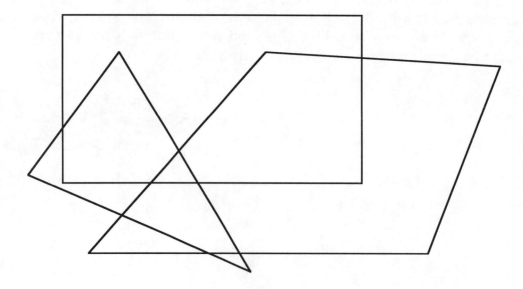

RATIO, PROPORTION, AND PERCENT

To the teacher

In most textbooks, percents, fractions, and decimals are taught separately. Yet when students see the connection between percents, fractions, and decimals, their skills seem to improve. Therefore, I like to teach percent with ratio and proportion; it helps students see that percent is another language for expressing a ratio, just like fractions and decimals.

I have included two problems where students need to diagram their knowledge of percents. It is never too late to ask students to represent a concept by a diagram—it does test their understanding.

MR. BARRY'S CLASS

In Mr. Barry's math class, you must correctly answer one proportion problem every day before you go to lunch. Could you eat lunch today?

On segment AC, AB = 8, AB:BC = 2:5. Find AC.

49 **TOM'S TIE**

Tom bought a tie at a fantastic sale. Find the original price if, after it was reduced by 85%, he paid only $30. Explain how you got your answer.

50   CONVINCE YOUR FRIEND

Convince your friend, by using a good drawing, that 66 2/3 % of 12 is the same as 8.

51   12.5%

Use a diagram to show why 12.5% of 24 is 3.

52   TERESITA'S DRESS

Teresita wanted to buy a dress for $50, but she decided to wait because she didn't have enough money. A week later, the price had gone up 20%. Now she definitely had to wait. A week later, she went back to the store, and the price had gone down 20% from the last price. Teresita bought the dress. What did she pay for it? Explain your answer.

53   ALEX'S CAR

One year, Alex bought an antique car for his birthday. During the first year he owned it, the value of the car gained 10%. During the second year, the value of the car gained another 15% from the previous year. If the value of his car is now $37,950.00, how much did Alex originally pay for his car?

PROBABILITY

To the teacher

Probability is best taught by experimenting. You must be careful, however, that students work with enough problems so they don't generalize probablility laws to different kinds of problems. There are many good books on probability with many wonderful activities—you can use the *Math Ties* method on your problem-solving day to do many of those activities. I have included only four types of problems that can be used during a problem-solving session, and all are best solved in groups.

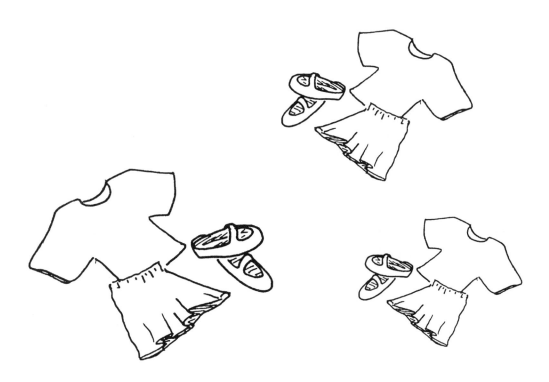

54   MATH

How many different three-letter code words can you make using the letters M, A, T, and H if you are not allowed to repeat any letters within each code word?

55   NOTHING TO WEAR!

A girl showed her friend five blouses, three skirts, and four pairs of shoes, all which match, but she complained to her mother that she had nothing to wear. Her mother told her that with all these garments she could wear a different outfit every day of the month. Was her mother correct? Explain your answer!

56   WHICH WAY TO GO?

"From Ithaca to Buffalo there are five routes that can be taken, from Buffalo to Niagara Falls there are two routes that can be taken, and from Niagara Falls to Toronto, Canada, there are three routes that can be taken," Dave said as he looked at his map, wondering which way to go. How many choices does Dave have? Can you make a diagram?

57   FOUR MAGIC NUMBERS

You must use four magic numbers: 4, 6, 0, and 5. You are not allowed to repeat them.

How many four-digit numbers can you make that are less than 5,000?

How many four-digit numbers can you make that are less than 1,000?

How many four-digit numbers can you make that are less than 6,000?

MAKE A DRAWING OR CHART

To the teacher

This section includes more problems that students can solve by making diagrams, charts, or tables. Many of the dreaded "train" or "motion" problems can also be solved by making a graph, so two such problems are included. Students will need you to model how to use a graph in solving these problems. "Train" problems can be incorporated in your linear equations unit, your unit on formulas (rate times time equals distance), or at any time during the year when you want your students to see the value of making graphs. You can use manipulatives to simulate the car or train.

For 61, Grandmother's Quilt, you may want to have students determine answers based on a variety of sizes of squares. It's amazing how many unique quilts can be drawn if the squares differ in size.

         © 1998 Critical Thinking Books & Software • www.criticalthinking.com • 800-458-4849

58   FIVE PEOPLE SHAKE HANDS

How many times can five people shake hands with one another? (The same 2 people shake only once.)

59   EIGHT PEOPLE SHAKE HANDS

How many times can eight people shake hands with one another? (The same 2 people shake only once.) Can you find a pattern?

60   A CIRCLE OF FRIENDS

If 28 friends sit in a circle, evenly spaced, who sits diagonally from person #2? (Hint: Look at a clock.)

61   GRANDMOTHER'S QUILT

Grandmother made a quilt of equally sized squares. Solid blue squares surround the edges of the quilt, and the inside squares are printed with yellow flowers. What size quilt did Grandmother make if her quilt had an equal number of solid blue and printed yellow flowered squares? Draw a good diagram to help you solve this problem.

62 THE OLD CAR AND THE NEW CAR

Alex left in his antique car at 10 A.M. going 30 m.p.h. At 11 A.M., his sister realized that he had left his wallet behind and went after him at 50 m.p.h. If they continued at those same rates, at what time of the day did she catch up with him? Finish this graph (or make a similar graph) to help you find the answer.

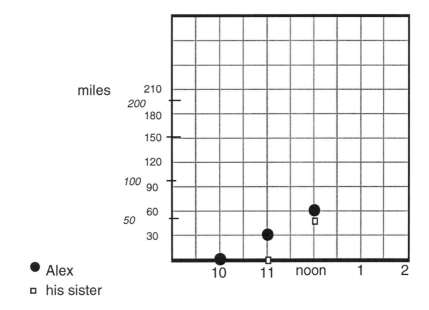

● Alex
□ his sister

63 THE OLD BUS AND THE NEW BUS

An old bus and a new bus left the same station heading in the same direction at 5 A.M. The old bus was going 40 m.p.h., and the new bus was going 50 m.p.h. If the buses kept going at those rates without stopping, how far apart were they at 10 A.M.? (Use a graph to help you.)

TOPOLOGY

To the teacher

Topology can be used to enrich your unit on geometry—your students will love to work with these problems. Many students will be surprised to find that some problems in this section may have more than one solution, and some have no solutions!

One of the most important goals in mathematics teaching is for students to value different views and solutions. Many cultures have had interesting views, some quite different from ours, on geometry. For Native Americans, the circle was an important figure. The Inuit people of the Canadian Arctic have very different views of time and space as well as size and shape; they are also very skilled at mapmaking. To find out more, you might want to read Chapter 2, Tracing Graphs in the Sand, of the book *Ethnomathematics* by Ascher.

The Konigsberg Bridge problem can be used to bring some history of mathematics into your classroom. In 1736, Euler was able to conclude that the problem had no solution. For information on the Euler Theorem, a series of four propositions about networks, see *History of Mathematics* by Howard Eves, p. 95.

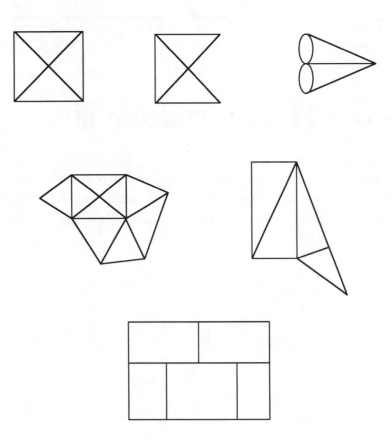

64 THE KONIGSBERG BRIDGE

The city of Konigsberg, in East Prussia, is located on the banks and two islands of the river Pregel. The parts of the city were connected by seven bridges as shown below. Is it possible to walk through all the bridges only once? (You are not allowed to swim, nor may you run or ride!)

A famous mathematician, Leonhard Euler (1707–83), wrote about this puzzle. The city of Konigsberg in the former Soviet Union was later known as Kaliningrad. You might want to see if you can find this city on a map or in an atlas.

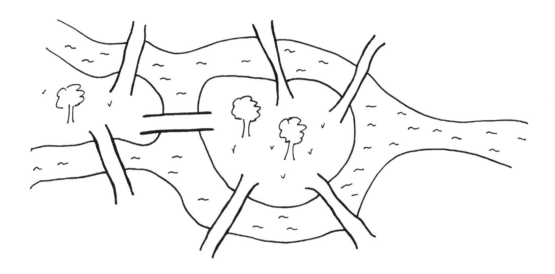

65 THE SPOOKY HOUSE

A spooky house has the floor plan shown below. A witch claims she can take an entire trip through this house and pass through each door once and only once. Can you do it? If you start on the inside you must end on the inside, and if you start on the outside you must end on the outside. Good Luck! (Don't forget to use a pencil with a good eraser!)

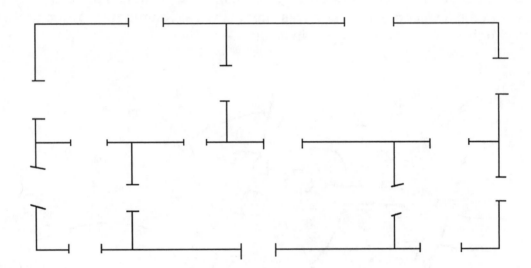

66 MIKE CALLAHAN'S PROBLEM

Can you color this design with at most four colors? No same colors can be side-by-side. It's okay for the same colors to touch at only one point.

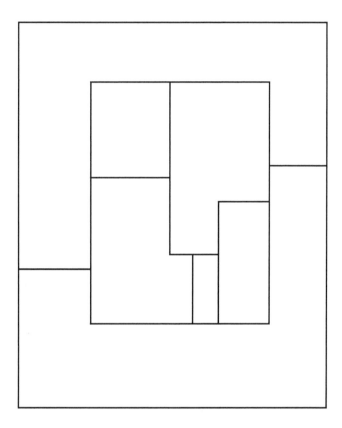

This design was made by Mike Callahan, a former student at DeWitt Middle School, in an attempt to create a "map" where more than four colors are needed to color it. Can you create your own "map" or design that would *require* more than four colors?

67   NETWORKS

The Shongo children from the Congo area in Africa love to copy and retrace figures drawn in the sand without lifting their finger or retracing any segment. Which of the following are possible to draw with a continuous line if retracing is not allowed?

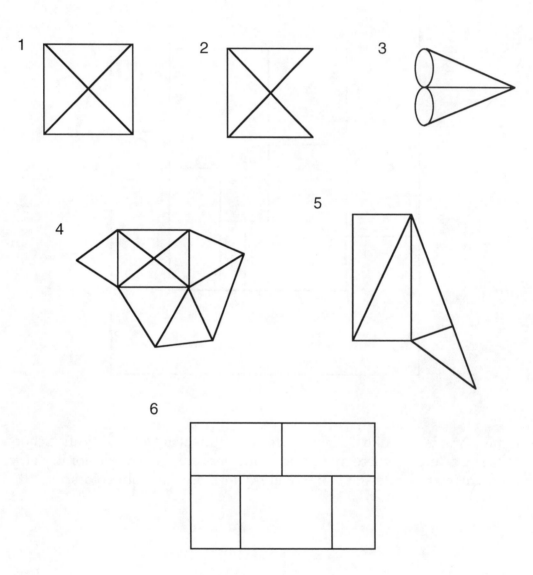

OTHER GREAT STRATEGY-AND-FUN PROBLEMS

INCLUDING TIME/CLOCK PROBLEMS

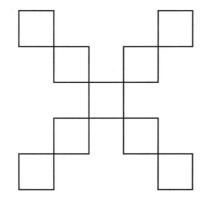

68   THE NINE DOTS

Connect all these dots without lifting your pencil and using only 4 straight lines. You may cross a line, but you may not trace over a line. It can be done!

69   THE TWENTY-FIVE DOTS

Connect these dots using only 8 straight lines without taking your pencil off the paper. You may cross a line, but you may not trace over a line. It can be done!

70 THE EIGHT DIGITS

Place each of the digits 1, 2, 3, 4, 5, 6, 7, and 8 in the eight boxes below so that the boxes that touch horizontally, vertically, or diagonally do *not* contain adjacent numbers (such as 3 and 4, etc.). Each of the eight digits must be used only once. Use a pencil!

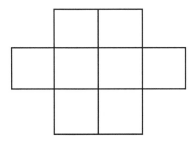

71 SUM OF 26

Place the digits 1–9 in each square below (without repetition) so that each pair of diagonals adds to 26 and the four corners also add to 26.

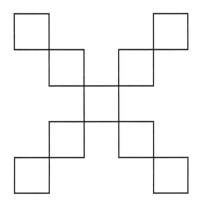

72   SLOW CLOCK

A clock loses 5 minutes every hour. If the clock is set at the correct time today, in how many days will it next show the correct time?

73   HARD-BOILED EGGS, ANYONE?

You have two egg timers. One takes 7 minutes for the sand in the top half to run to the bottom half, and the other takes 11 minutes. How can you use the two egg timers to time eggs that need to be boiled exactly 15 minutes? (You have no watch or clock to help you, and yes, you do love hard-boiled eggs!)

74   DAVE'S FAMOUS LEMON MERINGUE PIE

Dave, a great chef, has to bake a lemon meringue pie. The recipe says to bake it for exactly nine minutes. All Dave has for measuring time are two egg timers. The first one can measure only four minutes and the second one can measure only 7 minutes. There are no divisions or markings on the egg timers. How can Dave use these two egg timers to make his famous lemon meringue pie?

Answers

CROSSING THE RIVER

1. A Wolf, a Goat, and a Cabbage

Here is one solution: the ferryman takes the goat over, leaving the wolf with the cabbage (since the wolf does not eat cabbage). He returns to pick up the wolf then drops him on the other side but brings the goat back. Then he leaves the goat on the shore and picks up the cabbage. He takes the cabbage and drops it on the other side then comes back and gets the goat.

Here is another solution: the ferryman takes the goat over, comes back, and takes the cabbage to the other shore but brings the goat back. He drops off the goat, takes the wolf over, comes back, and takes the goat over.

2. The Three Jealous Husbands

It takes 9 trips. In the diagram below, H stands for Husband, and W stands for wife. Note that Wife 1 is not left alone on either shore or in the boat with another man. Wife 1 is picking up Wife 2.

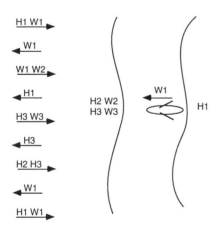

3. The Three Cats and the Three Mice

It takes 9 trips. This solution is similar to that of the previous problem.

4. The Four Middle School Students

The shortest time would be sixty minutes:

The 5- and 10-minute students go together first. Then the 5-minute person returns with the lantern and stays behind while the 20- and 25-minute students go together with the lantern. The 10-minute student returns to bring the lantern back, and then both the 5- and 10-minute students go back with the lantern:

First trip:	10 minutes
Second trip:	05 minutes
Third trip:	25 minutes
Fourth trip:	10 minutes
Last trip:	10 minutes
Total:	60 minutes

KIN PROBLEMS

5. From Bermuda

He is looking at his son. It may sound as if he were looking at himself, but if he were then "this man's father" (his own father) could not be his father's son.

6. From Puerto Rico

The sister of my aunt, who is not my aunt but is the daughter of my grandparents, is my mother.

7. From Wales

A brother-in-law to the only brother of our mother could be our father or stepfather. (A brother to our mother would be our uncle. His brother-in-law would be our father or stepfather.)

The answer could also be "no relation" if the brother is married and his wife has a brother. The wife's brother would be the brother-in-law to the brother of our mother, but be no relation to us.

8. From the United States

The sister-in-law of our father's only brother, who is unmarried, would be our mother.

9. From Brazil

One of the daughters is herself a mother. One of the women is a grandmother.

10. From Ireland

The third brother's own son is buried in the graveyard.

LOGIC PROBLEMS

11. The Three Intelligent Women

Her mark was black; the other women had white and black on their foreheads. Since all three women saw black dots, all three raised their hands. Let's call the winner #1, the other woman with black, #2, and the woman with white, #3. Woman #1 saw white and black. She knew #2 did not see her own (#2's) black dot, so #2 must have been raising her hand because she saw #1 with a black dot. The same explanation can be made for #2, so either #2 or #1, whoever answered first, is the lucky winner.

12. Who's Telling the Truth?

The guide was a truth-teller.

If the native asked was from the eastern side, he would have said "western," and the guide, if a truth-teller, would have reported "western." If the native asked was from the western side, he would have said "western," and the guide, if a truth teller, would also have said "western."

If the native asked was from the eastern side and the guide was dishonest , the native would have said "western" and the guide would have reported back "eastern." If the native asked was from the western side and the guide was dishonest, the native would have said "western" and the guide would have reported back "eastern." Since the guide reported back "western," the guide was a truth-teller.

13. Apples and Oranges

Since you can reach into only one box, reach into the "Apples & Oranges" box. If you get an orange, you know this box must be the "orange" box. The box labeled "apples" must be the "apples & oranges" box, and the one labeled "oranges" is the "apples" box. Similarly, if you reach into the "apples & oranges" box and you get an apple, then this must be the "apples" box, etc.

14. The Famous Card Problem

You need to turn the first card because it's blue and you want to know if it has a triangle on the other side. You don't need to turn the second card since it's yellow and it doesn't matter whether or not it has a triangle on the other side. You must turn the third card (the one with a circle) because if it is blue on the other side then not all blue cards have a triangle on the other side. You don't need to turn the last card, which already has a triangle: if it is blue it answers the question, but if it is another color it doesn't matter (it would not contradict the idea that every blue card has a triangle on the other side).

15. The Six Glasses

Pour the second glass into the fifth glass, and they will alternate.

EXPONENTS AND FRACTIONS

16. St. Ives

Including all the wives, sacks, cats, and kittens, 2800 went to St. Ives:

7	wives	(7^1)
49	sacks	(7^2)
343	cats	(7^3)
<u>2401</u>	kittens	(7^4)
2800		

Don't add the man—the problem asks only for wives, sacks, cats, and kittens.

17. Terri's Grandfather

Terri's grandfather is 72 years old. You can work backwards or use guess and check. You can also get the answer by using algebra:

$$1/4\,X + 1/6\,X + 1/2\,X + 6 = X$$

$$3\,X + 2\,X + 6\,X + 72 = 12\,X$$

$$11\,X + 72 = 12\,X$$

$$72 = X$$

18. Your Ancestors

You would entertain 2046 people. Add $2^1 + 2^2 + 2^3 \ldots + 2^{10}$

Here is a formula to get the grand total in one step: $2^{n+1} - 2$ (where n is the number of generations). The sum from 2^1 to 2^{10} is $2^{11} - 2 = 2046$.

19. A Plumbing Problem

One sixth of the water entering pipe 1 exits through pipe 4. $(1/4 \times 2/3 = 2/12, \text{or } 1/6)$

20. Bookworm

Make a diagram. Since the books are standing upright and in order, the first page of Volume I is at the right-hand side of the book and the last page of Volume 2 is at the left-hand side of that book! The worm has

to go through only two covers (back of first, front of second) at 1/8 inch each for a total of 1/4 inch.

PRE-ALGEBRA/ALGEBRA

21. Centi, The Centipede

December 7th. Count 9 days, including the first. (Remember that November has 30 days.)

22. The Baby Whale

The whale weighs 200 lbs. (Solve for x: $100 + 1/2\,x = x$, so $100 = 1/2\,x$)

23. Visiting Grandma

Since Elise's age is represented by one box, Gaby's age can be shown by two boxes, and Grandma's can be shown by 6. If nine boxes equals 90 years then Elise is 10, Gaby is 20, and Grandma is 60.

Elise	Gaby	Grandma
☐	☐☐	☐☐☐☐☐☐

24. Unusual Pet Shop

Of the pets, 17 are birds (34 legs), and 13 are dogs, (52 legs). The answer could be found by using a table. If you use algebra, you can let B stand for the number of birds and D stand for the number of dogs: $B + D = 30$ (so $B = 30 - D$) and $2B + 4D = 86$ (since birds have two legs and dogs have 4). Then $2 \times (30 - D) + 4D = 86$ and $60 - 2D + 4D = 86$ so $2D = 26$, making $D = 13$ dogs.

25. A Farmer's Problem

She picked 200 apples on the second day. Let x = the number of apples:

$$x + 2x + 4x = 700$$
$$7x = 700$$
$$x = 100$$

26. Jack and Jill's Book Problem

Jill has 14 books, Jack has 15. This could be found by trial and error (see chart) or with simultaneous equations.

Let x = Jack; let y = Jill:

$$x + y = 29$$
$$x - 3 + 2y = 40$$

Jack	Jill	Work
10	19	7 + 38 = 45
11	18	8 + 36 = 44
13	16	10 + 32 = 42
14	15	11 + 30 = 41
15	14	12 + 28 = 40

27. Another Day, Another Dollar

There is no dollar missing. This is an order of operations problem.

The cost of the car is $25 divided by 3, or 8 1/3 dollars for each. In addition, they each paid 2/3 dollar for the tip for a total of $9.00 each. In all, the women paid $27 including the tip. The $3.00 that would have made $30 was returned and split between them.

GEOMETRY

28. Thinking in Quarters

It takes 4 quarter-inch squares to make an inch square. It takes 64 quarter-inch cubes to make an inch cube.

29. A Carpenter's Problem

She needs to make 6 cuts (2 in each dimension).

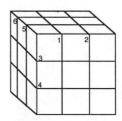

30. Cubes in the Corner

There are 10 cubes not visible.

If you try the problem with a bottom visible row of 5, the answer is 20 cubes not visible.

31. What Angle Is It?

The clock hands make an angle of 75° (not 90°, as the little hand is between 3 and 4). There is 12 1/2 minutes difference between the hands.

$$12.5/60 = x/360$$

32. Regions in a Circle

Here are the maximum numbers of regions into which a circle may be divided by 3, 4, and 5 straight lines:

3 straight lines: 7 regions

4 straight lines: 11 regions

5 straight lines: 16 regions

Starting with 1 line, 2 regions; 2 lines, 4 regions; etc., you can add 2 to the first answer, 3 to the second answer, then 4, etc.

33. The Missing Diameter

The diameter of the circle is 17 inches.

If BD = 8.5", CA is also 8.5" (both are diagonals of rectangle ABCD, and the diagonals of a rectangle are congruent). Since CA is also the radius of the circle, the diameter of the circle is 2 x 8.5", or 17 inches.

34. A Different View

The circumference of the semicircle is 4π meters. If the circle were whole, its radius would be 4 meters and its diameter 8 meters. The circumference of a circle is diameter times π, so if the circle were whole, its diameter would be 8π meters. The semicircle is half that, or 4π meters.

35. The Missing Perimeter

The perimeter is 100 units: $(20 \times 2) + (30 \times 2)$. In the diagram below, if we moved side D over until it was under side F and moved side E down alongside side C, we would have a rectangle. Side F-D would equal side B, and side E-C would equal side A. The perimeter would be the same as the original polygon: $30 + 30 + 20 + 20 = 100$.

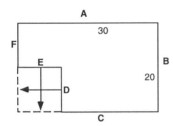

36. The Geometry Fly

The fly travels about 33.5 feet. Use the Pythagorean Theorem twice (you might ask students to round to the nearest tenth).

Find FC: $10^2 + 20^2 = FC^2$, $FC = \sqrt{500}$ feet. Then find EC: $EC^2 = 25^2 + 500$; EC is about 33.5 feet.

NUMBER THEORY

37. The Sum from 1 to 20

The sum is 210.

$1 +$	$2 +$	$3 +$	$4 +$	$5 +$	$6 +$	$7 +$	$8 +$	9	$+ 10$
$20 +$	$19 +$	$18 +$	$17 +$	$16 +$	$15 +$	$14 +$	$13 +$	12	$+ 11$
$21 +$	$21 +$	$21 +$	$21 +$	$21 +$	$21 +$	$21 +$	$21 +$	21	$+ 21$

The answer is $10 \times 21 = 210$.

You can add the least number to the greatest, the next least to the next greatest, etc. You get the same thing by dividing the total number of numbers by 2 and multiplying by the sum you would get from each pair.

38. The Sum from 1 to 99

The sum is 4950.

Use the same idea as in the last problem. You will pair

$1 + 99 = 100$

$2 + 98 = 100$

etc. You will have 49 pairs each totaling 100 for 4900, then add 50, the number in the middle to get 4950.

39. The Sum from 4 to 180

The sum is 16,284.

To see how to get the answer, use an easier problem: from 4 to 10, there are 7 numbers $(10 - 4 + 1)$. You can match $4 + 10$, $5 + 9$, and $6 + 8$ to get three sets of 14; then you have to add the middle number, 7.

From 4 to 180, there are 177 numbers $(180 - 4 + 1)$. You can match $4 + 180$, $5 + 179$, $6 + 178$, etc. and get $177 \div 2$, or 88 remainder 1. This translates to 88 pairs each adding to 184, plus the middle number, which is 92. Therefore, the answer must be $(88 \times 184) + 92 = 16,284$.

40. The First 50 Odd Numbers

The sum is 2500.

$1 + 3 = 4$, or 2^2

$1 + 3 + 5 = 9$, or 3^2

$1 + 3 + 5 + 7 = 16$, or 4^2

The sum of the first 50 odd numbers must be 50×50, or 50^2, which equals 2500.

41. The 450th Odd Number?

1st odd number: 1

2nd odd number: 3

3rd odd number: 5

4th odd number: 7

5th odd number: 9

450th odd number: 899

Using n to represent a number's ordinal place in the series (for 1st odd number n = 1, for 2nd odd number n = 2, etc.), each solution is two times n minus one, or $2n - 1$.

42. 2^{50} (Two to the 50th Power)

Start by listing what happens when you divide progressive powers of 2 by 3:

$2^1 \div 3 = 0$, remainder 2

$2^2 \div 3 = 1$, remainder 1

$2^3 \div 3 = 2$, remainder 2

$2^4 \div 3 = 5$, remainder 1, etc.

When the power is even, the remainders are always one.

43. The Census Taker

List all the possibilities for 3 factors of 36:

$6 + 6 + 1 =$ 13

$4 + 9 + 1 =$ 14

$2 + 18 + 1 =$ 21

$3 + 12 + 1 =$ 16

$6 + 2 + 3 =$ 11

$4 + 3 + 3 =$ 10

$2 + 9 + 2 =$ 13

Notice that two sets have sums of 13, which is why the census taker could not yet determine the answer. As soon as the lady said that the *oldest* child plays the piano, he knew the ages must be 2, 9, and 2 (the combination that has an eldest).

SET THEORY

44. The Sixth Grade Musical

There are 156 students in the sixth grade class. You can use subtraction to determine numbers of students taking band only, choir only, and orchestra only. For example, from the total number of students taking band, subtract those students taking band and choir, students taking band and orchestra, and students taking all three ($62 - 20 - 5 - 7 = 30$). See the diagram below. Don't forget to add the 20 who don't take band, orchestra, or choir!

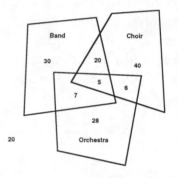

45. The Antique Button Collection

Mike's mother has 15 buttons in her collection.

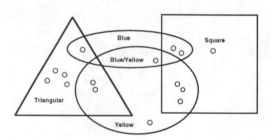

46. The Motor Club

There are 30 women in the motor club (see the following diagram).

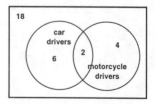

47. Create Your Own Sets Problem

Answers will vary.

RATIO, PROPORTION, & PERCENT

48. Mr. Barry's Class

You could eat today if you found that AC = 28.

8:BC = 2:5

2BC = 40, so BC = 20

Add AB to BC to get AC: 8 + 20 = 28.

49. Tom's Tie

The original price of the tie was $200.

Let the original price be x:

$$x - 85\%x = 30$$
$$1x - .85x = 30$$
$$.15x = 30$$
$$x = 200$$

50. Convince Your Friend

The following shows that 66 2/3% of 12 is 8 (remember that 66 2/3% is 2/3):

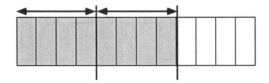

51. 12.5%

The following diagram shows that 12.5 of 24 is 3 (12.5% is one-eighth, and one-eighth of 24 is 3):

52. Teresita's Dress

Teresita paid $48.

Remember that 20% is the same as .2; adding 20% of 50 is the same as multiplying 50 by 120%, or 1.2; subtracting 20% of 60 is

the same as subtracting .2 times 60, or 1.2:

$50 x 1.2 = $60

$60 − .2 (60) = $48

53. Alex's Car

Alex paid $30,000 for his car.

x + .10x + .15 (1.10x) = 37,950 so x + .10x +.165 x = 37,950 or 1.265x = 37,950; therefore x = 30,000. You could also work backwards as below, since 37,950 is 115% of the previous years's value:

37,950/115 = x/100; x = 33,000

Similarly, 33,000/110 = x/ 100 and x = $30,000.

PROBABILITY

54. MATH

You can make 24 different code words.

The problem can be solved by using the permutations formula (n stands for the total number of items taken r at a time):

nPr = n!/(n–r)!

Therefore, 4!/(4–3)! = 4!/1! = 4 x 3 x 2 x 1 = 24.]

55. Nothing to Wear!

Yes, she could wear a different outfit every day of the month (multiply the numbers in each category):

5 x 3 x 4 = 60 outfits

56. Which Way to Go?

Dave has 30 choices. Multiply the number of possible routes in each leg of the trip: 5 x 2 x 3 = 30. (See the following diagram.)

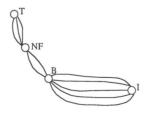

57. Four Magic Numbers

Four-digit numbers less than

5000:	12 (2 x 3 x 2 x 1)
1000:	6 (1 x 3 x 2 x 1)
6000:	18 (3 x 3 x 2 x 1)

Count the number of possible digits for each place. For numbers less than 5000, you can use 4 or 0 (one of <u>two</u> numbers) in the thousands place, one of the remaining <u>three</u> numbers in the hundreds place, one of the remaining <u>two</u> numbers in the tens place, and the <u>one</u> remaining number for the ones place.

MAKE A DRAWING OR CHART

58. Five People Shake Hands

Five people can shake hands with one another 10 times. Suppose the people are numbered 1–5: 1 shakes hands with 2, with 3, with 4, and with 5. That's 4 handshakes. Then 2 shakes with 3, with 4, and with 5. That's another 3 shakes. Then 3 shakes with 4 and with 5 for another 2 shakes. Finally, 4 shakes with 5 for 1 more. 4 + 3 + 2 + 1 = 10.

59. Eight People Shake Hands

Eight people can shake hands with one another 28 times.

The following pattern emerges:

No. of persons	Handshakes
1	0
2	1
3	3
4	6
5	10
6	15
7	21
8	28

The answer becomes n(n–1) / 2 where n = number of persons.

60. A Circle of Friends

Person 16 sits diagonally across from person 2:

61. Grandmother's Quilt

Here are two solutions:

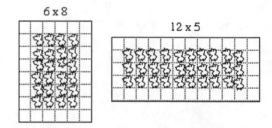

62. The Old Car and the New Car

Alex's sister catches up with him at 12:30 P.M. By 1.5 hours after the sister starts, both cars would have traveled 75 miles. The solution is shown where both lines meet (one represents Alex's trip and one represents his sister's trip).

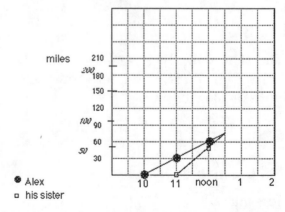

63. The Old Bus and the New Bus

The buses were 50 miles apart. By using a

graph or a chart, you can keep track of the distance traveled every hour:

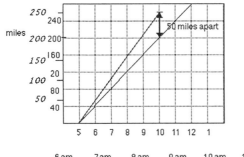

	6 am	7 am	8 am	9 am	10 am	11 am
	40	80	120	160	200	250
	50	100	150	200	250	300

50 miles apart

TOPOLOGY

64. The Konigsberg Bridge

Unless you swim the channel or jump (instead of walk) across bridges, etc., there is no solution.

65. The Spooky House

Sorry, there is no solution!

66. Mike Callahan's Problem

Here is one solution:

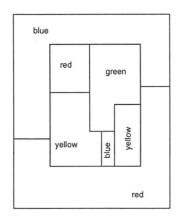

67. Networks

It is possible to draw figures 2 and 5 without lifting the pencil or retracing.

OTHER GREAT STRATEGY-AND-FUN PROBLEMS

68. The Nine Dots

Start at the lower left as shown below:

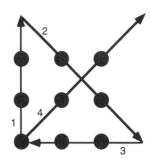

69. The Twenty-Five Dots

Start at the upper left, as shown below:

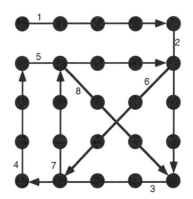

70. The Eight Digits

There is a strategy here. The greatest and least numbers, 1 and 8, have only one other number that is consecutive (1 with 2, 8 with 7); therefore, place the 1 and 8 in the center.

	4	6	
7	1	8	2
	3	5	

71. Sum of 26

Two solutions follow; for all solutions, 7 must be in the center.

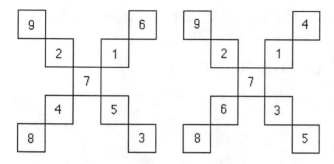

72. Slow Clock

It will show the correct time in 6 days. Since it loses 5 minutes per hour, it will be one hour behind every twelve hours. It will take 12 times 12, or 144, hours, which is 6 days, to show the correct time again.

73. Hard-boiled Eggs, Anyone?

Turn both timers over. When the 7-minute timer runs out, you know there are still 4 minutes left on the 11-minute timer. Start boiling eggs at this point. Wait until the 11-minute timer runs out (4 minutes) then turn it over again. When the 11-minute timer runs out the second time, 15 minutes have passed, so stop boiling the eggs.

74. Dave's Famous Lemon Meringue Pie

Here is one solution: Turn both timers over. When the 4-minute timer runs out, there are 3 minutes left in the 7-minute timer; turn the 4-minute timer over again. When the 7-minute timer runs out, 3 minutes have passed and there is 1 minute left on the 4-minute timer. Start baking. When the 1 minute is up, turn the 4-minute timer over again; when it is up, turn it again. When the 4-minute timer runs out once more, 9 minutes have passed, so take the pie out of the oven.

Appendix A

PROBLEM-SOLVING PORTFOLIO

Note to the teacher

The Problem-Solving Portfolio can be used as an aid to self-analysis, encouraging students to take time to reflect on their problem-solving growth. It can also be used as an evaluation tool, but be careful not to make the portfolio itself the goal of problem solving.

Read the directions to the students, and provide time for students to answer the questions individually. Students should attach the appropriate problem to each questionnaire and make an attractive cover. Allow students to include problems they got wrong, if they wish, as long as they correct the original errors. The emphasis should be on effort.

A rubric for evaluating the Problem-Solving Portfolio has been provided for your convenience.

PROBLEM-SOLVING PORTFOLIO

DIRECTIONS

   I. Choose three problems according to the following categories.

      1. Most fun

      2. Most challenging

      3. Problem that clearly demonstrates one or more problem-solving strategies

      NOTE: All problems should have the correct work and answer.

  II. Fill out the questionnaires and attach each one to the appropriate problem. Write neatly in complete sentences.

 III. Make an attractive cover. Label it with "PROBLEM-SOLVING PORTFOLIO," your name, and your class period.

MOST FUN PROBLEM

Name of the problem _____

What made this problem fun? _____

_____

What strategy(ies) did you or your group use to solve this problem? _____

_____

_____

How did any of those strategies help you? _____

_____

_____

Was this problem fun to do in a group, or individually? Explain. _____

_____

_____

Do you think you did better on this problem because it was more fun than other problems?

Explain. _____

_____

_____

_____

Other comments:

_____

_____

_____

_____

MOST CHALLENGING PROBLEM

Name of the problem _____

What made this problem most challenging? _____
_____

How did you figure out how to start? _____
_____

Did you get the answer the first time you did it? _____
_____

If at first you did not get the answer, how did you proceed? _____
_____

How did it help to solve this problem in a group? _____
_____

What problem-solving strategy(ies) helped you or your team to solve this problem?
_____

How did the strategy(ies) help you? _____
_____

Did it help you to know that you were not being graded on your answer? In other words, if you had to solve a similar problem on a test, would you feel anxious and fear you might not get the answer? _____
_____

Do you consider yourself a good problem solver? _____ Explain why or why not, using the back of this page if necessary. _____
_____

PROBLEM THAT BEST DEMONSTRATES THE USE OF PROBLEM-SOLVING STRATEGIES

Give the name of the problem that best demonstrates your use of problem-solving strategies.

_____

What strategy did you use? _____

_____

_____

How did the strategies help you? _____

_____

Did you seek help from any of your team members? Explain. _____

_____

_____

Tell something you learned about math or about yourself by doing this problem. _____

_____

_____

Do you think you work best independently or with others? _____

_____

In a problem-solving situation, do you consider yourself a leader or a follower? Explain.

_____

Is problem solving easier or harder for you this year when compared to other years? (Use the back of this page if necessary.) _____

_____

_____

_____

RUBRIC FOR PROBLEM-SOLVING EVALUATION

NAME _____ PERIOD _____

_____ Choice of problems according to categories (1–3)

_____ Questionnaire—effort, complete sentences, neatness (1–5)

_____ Effort shown on problems (1–5)

_____ Cover (1–2)

_____ Total points (15 total)

_____ **Portfolio grade**

Comments _____

_____

_____

_____

Appendix B

MATH MYTHS

Read each of the following and answer honestly. Check each statement that you agree with. Be ready to support your answers.

_____ 1. Mathematics ability is inherited.

_____ 2. You don't need to study for math.

_____ 3. Reading, writing, and spelling are not important in mathematics.

_____ 4. Boys are better than girls in math or science.

_____ 5. Problem solving is the hardest part of mathematics.

_____ 6. If you don't know how to solve a problem after you read it, you probably don't know enough to solve it.

_____ 7. If you don't understand something in math, it usually means you're not good in math.

_____ 8. If you ask questions in math class, people will think that you are either a "nerd" or just "slow."

_____ 9. Math is easy only when the teacher is reviewing old stuff.

_____ 10. Taking notes in math class is not as important as taking notes in other subjects.

_____ 11. Only those gifted in math or science are able to become mathematicians or scientists.

_____ 12. Mathematicians and scientists don't enjoy sports or other subjects as much as the rest of the population does.

Appendix C

MATRIX OF PROBLEM-SOLVING CONCEPTS

PROBLEM NUMBER

CONCEPTS	1	2	3	4	5	6	7	8	9	10	11	12	13	14	15	16	17	18	19	20	21	22	23	24
Whole Numbers/Exponents	✓	✓	✓	✓												✓								
Fractions																	✓	✓	✓	✓				
Pre-Algebra/Algebra																								
Negative Numbers																					✓			
Order of Operations																								
Equations																						✓	✓	
Systems of Equations																								✓
Geometry																								
Perimeter																								
Area																								
Volume																								
Angles																								
Polygons																								
Circles																								
Pythagorean Theorem																								
Number Theory																								
Patterns																								
Factors and Multiples																								
Sets																								
Ratio, Proportion & Percent																								
Probability																								
Logic	✓	✓	✓	✓	✓	✓	✓	✓	✓	✓				✓	✓									
Topology																								

MATRIX OF PROBLEM-SOLVING CONCEPTS

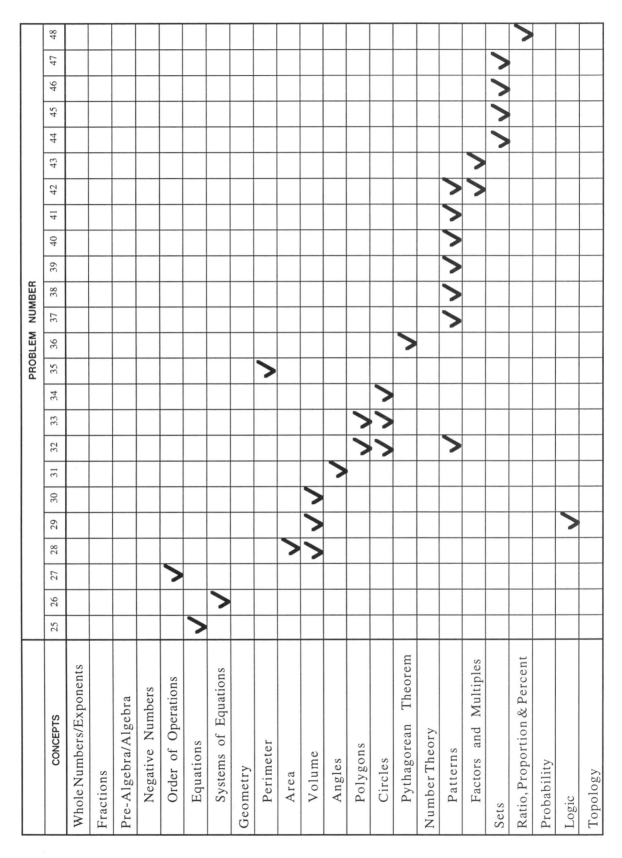

PROBLEM NUMBER

CONCEPTS	25	26	27	28	29	30	31	32	33	34	35	36	37	38	39	40	41	42	43	44	45	46	47	48
Whole Numbers/Exponents	✓																							
Fractions																								
Pre-Algebra/Algebra																								
Negative Numbers																								
Order of Operations			✓																					
Equations		✓																						
Systems of Equations																								
Geometry																								
Perimeter											✓													
Area				✓	✓	✓																		
Volume				✓																				
Angles							✓																	
Polygons								✓	✓															
Circles									✓	✓														
Pythagorean Theorem												✓												
Number Theory																								
Patterns								✓					✓	✓	✓	✓	✓	✓						
Factors and Multiples																		✓	✓					
Ratio, Proportion & Percent																				✓	✓	✓	✓	
Probability																								✓
Logic					✓																			
Topology																								

MATRIX OF PROBLEM-SOLVING CONCEPTS

PROBLEM NUMBER

CONCEPTS	49	50	51	52	53	54	55	56	57	58	59	60	61	62	63	64	65	66	67	68	69	70	71	72	73	74
Whole Numbers/Exponents																						✓	✓	✓		
Fractions																										
Pre-Algebra/Algebra																										
Negative Numbers																										
Order of Operations																										
Equations														✓	✓											
Systems of Equations																										
Geometry																										
Perimeter													✓	✓												
Area																										
Volume																										
Angles																										
Polygons																										
Circles																										
Pythagorean Theorem																										
Number Theory																										
Patterns										✓	✓															
Divisibility																										
Sets																										
Ratio, Proportion & Percent	✓	✓	✓	✓	✓	✓	✓	✓	✓																	
Probability												✓		✓	✓											
Logic																✓	✓	✓	✓	✓	✓				✓	✓
Topology																✓	✓	✓	✓							

Appendix D

MATRIX OF PROBLEM-SOLVING STRATEGIES

PROBLEM NUMBER

STRATEGIES	1	2	3	4	5	6	7	8	9	10	11	12	13	14	15	16	17	18	19	20	21	22	23	24
Make diagram, chart, or table	✓	✓	✓	✓	✓	✓	✓	✓	✓	✓	✓	✓	✓	✓	✓	✓	✓	✓	✓	✓	✓	✓	✓	✓
Try easier numbers																								
Find a pattern or formula						✓										✓	✓	✓				✓		✓
Act it out!	✓	✓	✓	✓	✓	✓	✓	✓	✓	✓	✓	✓	✓	✓	✓	✓				✓			✓	
Use manipulatives		✓	✓	✓							✓		✓	✓	✓						✓	✓	✓	
Work backwards																								
Guess and check												✓	✓	✓	✓		✓						✓	✓
Explore other answers					✓		✓	✓			✓				✓	✓							✓	

PROBLEM NUMBER

STRATEGIES	25	26	27	28	29	30	31	32	33	34	35	36	37	38	39	40	41	42	43	44	45	46	47	48
Make diagram, chart, or table	✓	✓	✓	✓	✓	✓	✓	✓	✓	✓	✓	✓	✓	✓	✓	✓	✓	✓	✓	✓	✓	✓	✓	✓
Try easier numbers														✓	✓	✓	✓							
Find a pattern or formula	✓	✓				✓		✓	✓	✓			✓	✓	✓	✓	✓	✓	✓					✓
Act it out!		✓	✓	✓	✓																			
Use manipulatives				✓		✓	✓					✓									✓	✓	✓	
Work backwards																								
Guess and check	✓	✓				✓	✓	✓			✓											✓		✓
Explore other answers																								

MATRIX OF PROBLEM-SOLVING STRATEGIES

PROBLEM NUMBER

STRATEGIES	49	50	51	52	53	54	55	56	57	58	59	60	61	62	63	64	65	66	67	68	69	70	71	72	73	74
Make diagram, chart, or table	✓	✓		✓	✓	✓	✓	✓	✓	✓	✓	✓	✓	✓	✓	✓	✓	✓	✓	✓	✓			✓	✓	✓
Try easier numbers				✓	✓					✓	✓	✓														
Find pattern or formula	✓			✓	✓	✓	✓			✓	✓	✓		✓	✓		✓					✓		✓		
Act it out!											✓	✓														
Use manipulatives		✓	✓			✓	✓	✓	✓	✓	✓	✓	✓	✓	✓	✓		✓	✓	✓	✓			✓	✓	✓
Work backwards	✓				✓																					
Guess and check	✓	✓	✓							✓	✓	✓	✓			✓	✓			✓	✓	✓	✓			
Explore other answers	✓		✓	✓									✓				✓	✓	✓	✓	✓		✓			

Bibliography

Included are books I've used over the years and a few resources to get you started in collecting more problems. I've listed a few of the many great sources on the worldwide web—they will take you to many other links. Also, don't overlook your public library.

Ary, Daniel W. *Middle School Math Challenge.* Santa Barbara, CA: The Learning Works, Inc. 1995.

Ascher, Marcia. *Ethnomathematics.* Pacific Grove, CA: Brooks/Cole Publishing Co., 1991.

Averbach, Bonnie and Orin Chein. *Mathematics Problem Solving Through Recreational Mathematics.* San Francisco,CA: W.H.Freeman and Company, 1980.

Burns, Marilyn. *The I Hate Mathematics! Book.* Little, Brown, 1976.

Dolciani, Mary, et al. *Structure and Method. Course I.* Boston: Houghton Mifflin Co., 1985.

Edwards, Ronald. *Algebra Magic Tricks. Algecadabra!* Volume 1. Pacific Grove: Critical Thinking Press and Software, 1992.

Eves, Howard. *An Introduction to the History of Mathematics*, 3rd ed. New York: Holt, Rinehart and Winston, 1969.

Fisher, Lyle. *Problems of the Week.* Palo Alto, CA: Dale Seymour Publications, 1981.

Fixx, James F. *Games for the Super Intelligent.*London: Frederick Muller Limited, 1972.

Fixx, James F. *More Games for the Super Intelligent.* New York: Popular Library, CBS Publications, 1977.

Fixx, James F. *Solve It! A Perplexing Profusion of Puzzles.* Garden City, NY: Doubleday & Co., Inc., 1978.

Fujii, John N. *Puzzles & Graphs.* Washington, D.C., National Council of Teachers of Mathematics, 1966.

Gardner, Martin. *Entertaining Mathematical Puzzles.* Mineola, NY: Dover Publications, 1961.

Hamilton, Ben. *Brainteasers and Mindbenders.* Englewood Cliffs, NY: Prentice-Hall, Inc., 1981.

Hunter, J.A.H. *Mathematical Brain-Teasers.* New York: Dover Publications, Inc., 1976.

Kraitchik, Maurice. *Mathematical Recreations.* New York: Dover Publications, Inc., 1953.

Lake, Frances and Joseph Newmark. *Mathematics as a Second Language.* 2nd ed. New York: Addison-Wesley Publishing Co., 1978.

Lewis, David B. *Eureka! Math Fun From Many Angles.* New York: The Putnam Publishing Co., 1953.

Longley-Cook, L.H. *New Math Puzzle Book.* New York: Van Nostrand Reinhold Co., 1970.

Lukacs, C. and E. Tarjam. *Mathematical Games*. New York: Walker and Company, 1968.

Menaker. F.E. *How Smart Are You?*. New York: Leisure League of America, 1935.

Multiculturalism in Mathematics, Science and Technology: Readings and Activities. New York: Addison-Wesley Publishing Co., 1993.

Phillips, Louis. *263 Brain Busters. Just How Smart Are You Anyway?* New York: Viking Penguin, Inc., 1985.

Polya, George. *How To Solve It*. Princeton: Princeton University Press, 1957.

Problem Solving In School Mathematics. 1980 Yearbook of the National Council of Teachers of Mathematics, Reston, VA: NCTM, 1980.

Seymour, Dale. *Favorite Problems*. Palo Alto, CA: Dale Seymour Publications, 1982.

Shulte, Albert P. and Stuart A. Choate. *What Are My Chances?* Book B. Palo Alto, CA: Creative Publications, 1977.

Smullyan, Raymond M. *What is the Name of this Book? The Riddle of Dracula and Other Logical Puzzles*. New York: Simon & Schuster, Inc., 1986.

Swartz, Robert J. and Sandra Parks. *Infusing the Teaching of Critical and Creative Thinking Into Content Instruction*. Pacific Grove, CA: Critical Thinking Books and Software, 1994.

Tobias, Sheila. *Overcoming Math Anxiety*. New York: W.W. Norton & Co., 1978.

Yawin, R.A. *Math Games and Puzzles*. Middletown, Co: Xerox Education Publications, 1976.

Zaslavsky, Claudia. *Africa Counts. Number and Pattern in African Culture*. Boston, MA: Prindle, Weber & Schmidt, Inc., 1973.

Zaslavsky, Claudia. *Math Comes Alive. Activities From Many Cultures*. Portland, ME: J. Weston, Publisher, 1987.

Zaslavsky, Claudia. *Tic Tac Toe and Other Three-In-A-Row Games*. NY: Thomas Y. Crowell, 1982.

Web sites

Aims Puzzle Corner. @ Aims Educational Foundation 1997. [Online] Available: http://www.aimsedu.org/PuzzleList.html

Brown, Joan Marie. *A Math Website for Middle School Students*. [Online] Available: http://www-personal.umd.umich.edu/~jobrown/math.html

Houghton Mifflin Mathematics Center. [Online] Available: http://www.eduplace.com/math/brain/

Husted, Terri. *A HomePage for New Math Teachers. Great Sites.* [Online] Available:
http://www.clarityconnect.com/webpages/terri/sites.html

Yahoo Math Puzzles. [Online] Available:
http://www.yahoo.com/Science/Mathematics/Games/Puzzles/